BEING A CHRISTIAN

A study book for children

by

David Walters

Illustrated by Dave Odell

Graphics Design and Layout by Judith A. Gilbert

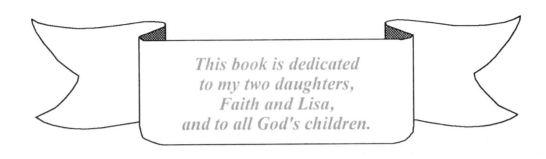

This book is dedicated to my two daughters, Faith and Lisa, and to all God's children.

Published by
GOOD NEWS FELLOWSHIP MINISTRIES
220 Sleepy Creek Rd.
Macon, GA 31210
Phone: 912-757-8071 Fax: 912-757-0136

International Standard Book Number: 0-9629559-2-2

Other Titles by David Walters

Kids in Combat—Training children and youth to be powerful for God.(For parents, teachers and youth pastors)

Equipping the Younger Saints—Raising Godly children and teaching them spiritual gifts. (For parents, teachers and youth pastors)

Children Aflame—Amazing Accounts of children from the journals of the great Methodist preacher John Wesley in the 1700's and David's own accounts with children and youth today.

The Anointing and You—What we must do to Receive, Sustain, Bring ,Impart, and Channel the Anointing for Renewal/Revival, and to pass it on to the Younger Generation.

Children's Bible Studies by David Walters

Armor of God - Illustrated children's Bible study of Ephesians 6: l0 - 18. (For children ages 6-15 years)

Fact or *Fantasy?* - Illustrated children's study in Christian apologetics. (For children ages 9- 15 years)

The Fruit of the Spirit - Illustrated children's Bible study on bearing fruit. (For children ages 7-15 years)

Printed by: **Faith Printing**
4210 Locust Hill Road
Taylors, S.C. 29687

Children who do not have Christian parents or never go to church usually don't know what a Christian is, and some of them don't even care. Then there are some who think they know, but they are often more wrong than right.

One of the ways the Bible defines a Christian is found in II Corinthians 5:17.

"If anyone is a Christian
   they are a NEW CREATURE,
      old things are passed away, watch and see,
         all things have become new."

Has that happened to you?

YES! NO! I DON'T KNOW! MAYBE! KIND OF! SORT OF!

If you have been raised in the Church or come to church regularly with your parents, you should know what it means to be a Christian — then you can tell those that don't know and help them to become Christians. Most young people who go to church **"sort of know"** what a Christian is. They have learned through Sunday school or children's church to give the right answers, *but* . . . . .

> ## being able to give the right answers *isn't* good enough.

WHY? You ask!

**"Isn't that why we come to church —
to learn about God . . .
and give the answers the teachers want to hear?"**

Well! It is true that your teachers like to hear you give the correct answer to the questions they ask — that means you are paying attention and learning the lessons. Being a Christian, however, is more than giving right answers. You see, **the Devil knows enough about being a Christian to give the right answers,** *a n d* **everybody knows**

he is *<u>absolutely not</u>* a Christian.

QUESTIONS FOR YOU TO ANSWER!

1. What does the Bible say a Christian is in II Corinthians 5:17?   *Circle the correct answer.*

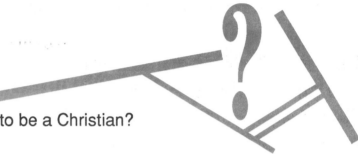

    A. A nicer person
    B. A religious creature
    C. A popular person
    D. A new creature
    E. An average guy

2. Why should you know what it means to be a Christian?

Answer:_____

3. What is the most important thing we need to learn at church?   *Circle the correct answer.*

    A. To read Bible stories
    B. To give the right answers
    C. To become a new creature
    D. To please our teachers

4. If each of the following people gave the right answers about being a Christian, which one of them would be a true Christian?   *Circle the correct answer.*

    A. The mailman
    B. The Devil
    C. Saddam Hussian
    D. The new creature
    E. The kid in children's church

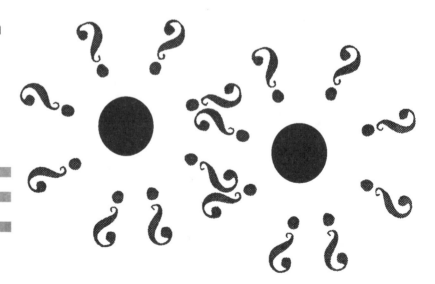

I preach to lots of young people all over the country and I have noticed that most of them are still *trying* to be Christians. Many of them think that if they can obey this rule or that rule and get all their answers correct that will make them real Christians. Somehow these young folks just don't seem to be quite good enough to get it all together — but they keep on trying.

Other kids begin to think its too hard and give up trying to be a Christian. They start behaving like their non-Christian friends who live in their neighborhood or go to their school.

The word **"Gospel"** means **GOOD NEWS.**

But it doesn't sound like the Gospel or **"good news"** to me when so many young people are struggling or have even given up trying to be a Christian.

They just haven't understood what a Christian is.

If I were to ask a young boy, "Are you a boy?" and he said, "Well, I'm trying to be one," or if I were to ask a teenage girl if she was a girl and she said, "Sort of I guess," you would think they were really weird.

Well, that is often the kind of answer I get when I ask kids if they are Christians.

A **B I G MISTAKE** that many kids make is that they don't realize —

IT IS G O D WHO MAKES US A CHRISTIAN, WE CANNOT DO IT OURSELVES!

You see, **WE ARE NOT BORN CHRISTIAN,** **we cannot make ourselves Christian**, – no matter how hard we try.

NOT Parents — **NOT** Teachers — **NOT** Preachers
can make us Christians,

In John 1:12-13 we read, "But as many (children and adults alike) as received Him, (Jesus) they have been given the right to become the children of God."

Those who believe in the name of Christ — they have become Christians –
- *not through blood,* (we are not born Christians through natural birth)
- *nor of the will of the flesh,* (we cannot make ourselves Christian by trying)
- *nor the will of man,* (others trying to make you a Christian)

but of God (born supernaturally by God's power).

Most church children and adults know the Ten Commandments, but are not able to keep them. Oh they *try* to, but always end up messing up one way or another. Did you know the Bible does not say we should *try* to love our neighbor, or we should *try* not to steal or tell lies. It says the commandments must be kept and not broken. You see, **the commandments were given by God to show us our weakness and our *inability* to keep them** (Romans 3:19-20). When we recognize that, then **we must trust in Jesus Christ who kept all the commandments and never broke one** — He did that for us. **In Gods eyes we have kept all the commandments;** *if Jesus Christ lives and reigns in our hearts and lives* (Romans 8:1-2).

THE COMMANDMENTS

YOU CAN'T KEEP ME!

Isn't that wonderful!

8

QUESTIONS FOR YOU TO ANSWER!

1. What does the word "gospel" mean? *Circle the correct answer.*

   A. The truth
   B. The Bible
   C. Good news
   D. Parables
   E. Scripture words

2. How hard must you try to become a real Christian? *Circle the correct answer.*

   A. A lot
   B. A little
   C. Not too little and not too much
   D. Not at all

3. How can we be made into Christians?

   A. By being born of Christian parents
   B By being born of rich parents
   C. By being born of God
   D. By being born of Godly parents
   E. By trying hard
   F. By being prayed for by an evangelist

4. Why were the Ten Commandments given?

   A. So that we should keep them
   B. So that we should break them
   C. So that we should ignore them
   D. To expose our weakness and sinfulness
   E. So that we should try to keep them

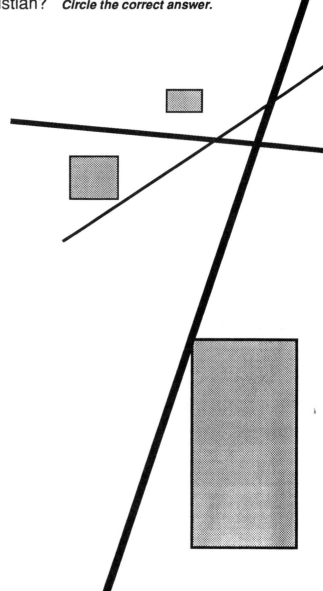

Children! • • • • • • •

The only way you can become a Christian is when you have a supernatural experience of **God's awesome power** which **gives** you **eternal life**. **ETERNAL** *means* **FOREVER — EVERLASTING**. This happens when you **believe**. When I say believe, I mean really believe. **Really, Really believe**. This kind of believing is not the kind you do just to please your parents or keep the Sunday school teachers off your back, but it is the kind of believing that makes you step out and dare to be different from the other kids, even your brothers and sisters. It is the kind of faith that **trusts Jesus with all of your heart** so much that you are willing to pay whatever it will cost you to be His disciple.

This is _not_ a wimpy "Kind of — Sort of" believing that many kids have today . . .

- **It is the kind of FAITH that we would be willing to *die* for if we had to.**

- **It means hanging on to Jesus and not letting go.** *The Bible says, ...*

"If you confess with your mouth Jesus as Lord, and believe in your heart that God has raised Him from the dead, you will be saved."

Romans 10:9.

When your heart has been changed from the inside, then your mouth will tell everyone about it. When you commit yourself to Him that much — He takes over and ***never*** lets you go. It is kind of strange that when you do this, you suddenly find that He is the One that is doing it all and you are just be-lieving — **then you begin to find out that even the faith and believing you have is coming from Him.**

Jesus is Lord!

QUESTIONS FOR YOU TO ANSWER!

1. What is the only way we can become a Christian?   *Circle the correct answer.*

    A. By hanging in there and staying faithful
    B. By receiving God's supernatural power
    C. By being first in a Bible quiz
    D. By speaking in tongues

2. How do we receive God's supernatural awesome power in our lives?
    Circle the correct answer.

    A. By prayer and fasting
    B. By obeying your parents
    C. By being the best in sports
    D. By really believing

3. What kind of believing does God expect from us?   *Circle the correct answer.*

    A. That which pleases our parents
    B. That which trusts God with all of our hearts
    C. That which pleases our Sunday school teacher
    D. A wimpy "sort of" believing

4. What are we to confess with our mouths?   *Circle the correct answer.*

    A. Our problems
    B. The Lord Jesus
    C. The Devil
    D. Bad words
    E. Lies

When Jesus died on the cross, He died for our sins. He took our punishment — which was death. We deserved to die and go to hell, yet He loved us so much that He died in our place. Jesus did not deserve to die. You see, we can't have our sins forgiven by taking our own punishment — that would mean our death. So that we all would not die, God needed someone to pay the price of sin for us. He needed a person who was innocent. That person had to be without any sins of his own — he had to be totally blameless thus never needing punishment himself.

Only Jesus was innocent, He took *our* punishment.

WE DESERVED TO DIE!

PAID IN FULL!

HE DIED IN OUR PLACE!

14

Everything that God does is perfect.

Although God sent Jesus to die for us, He doesn't expect us to please Him with the way we live, even though we may be forgiven. **Our lives can never please God** for they are not perfect enough and we keep messing up. That is why **Jesus must also live for us**. He does this by **living in us** as we invite Him in.

Jesus died for us, but that is only half of the deal –	THE OTHER HALF	is — He rose again for us. That is why He must also live for us.

This means He does it all as we simply allow Him too. *This is why people get baptized.* They bury their old sinful life under the water and they rise up out of the water in Christ's perfect life (Romans 6:4). They can only do that if they have been crucified with Christ (Galatians 2:20). How can you do that? You might ask, "Do I have to die?" **YES!** But not in a physical way. We have to die to our own selfish ways of wanting to be first. We must make Jesus number one and others second and ourself last. To do this is very hard isn't it?

Buried Old Life

Risen With Christ

Jesus put it this way...

"If anyone desires to come after Me, let him deny himself, (deny means to resist the desire to do what you want) and take up His cross, (a symbol of death) and follow ME. For whoever desires to save his life (do his own thing) will lose it, and whoever loses his life (doing God's will) for My sake will find it."

Matthew 16:24-25

Many Christians down through the years have called this . . . *SURRENDER.*

Think of two men wrestling and one has the other in a headlock so that he has to give up (submit). Now imagine yourself wrestling with the angel of the Lord — you would have to surrender to him too. As you can see, once we have surrendered to God we are *no longer trying* to be Christians — we **ARE** Christians.

By surrendering our life to God, we have accepted the gift of eternal life

which enables God's mighty spirit to dwell in us.

QUESTIONS FOR YOU TO ANSWER!

1. Who was punished for our sins?   *Circle the correct answer.*

   A. We were
   B. The Devil was
   C. Jesus was
   D. The angels were

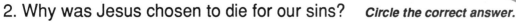

2. Why was Jesus chosen to die for our sins?   *Circle the correct answer.*

   A. Because He was sinless
   B. Because He loved us
   C. Because the Devil forced Him
   D. Because He was a great religious teacher

3. Why did Jesus rise again for us?   *Circle the correct answer.*

   A. To show us how to live
   B. So that we can follow His example
   C. So that He can live for us
   D. So that we can try to live for Him

4. How does Jesus live for us?   *Circle the correct answer.*

   A. By living in us
   B. By reigning in Heaven
   C. By helping us
   D. By watching us

5. What do we have to do to be baptized?   *Circle the correct answer.*

    A. Take a shower first
    B. Learn how to hold our breath
    C. See ourselves as crucified and dead
    D. Take a study course

6. What happens when you rise out of the water of baptism?   *Circle the correct answer.*

    A. You find yourself wet
    B. You get out of your wet clothes and dry off
    C. You feel clean
    D. You rise up in Christ's perfect life

7. What do Christians mean by "surrender"?   *Circle the correct answer.*

    A. Making Jesus first and self last
    B. Letting the Devil win
    C. Giving in to temptation
    D. Obeying your parents
    E. Being beaten by someone bigger than you

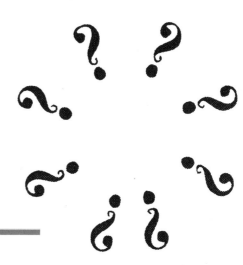

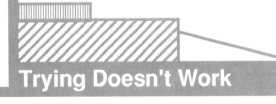

All too often people think they can make themselves into a Christian by doing certain things, but *the Bible says* . . .

> **"FOR BY *GRACE* YOU HAVE BEEN SAVED *THROUGH FAITH*; AND THAT NOT OF YOURSELVES, IT IS THE GIFT OF GOD, NOT OF WORKS, THAT NO ONE SHOULD BOAST."**
> *EPHESIANS 2:8-9*

Have you ever taken an exam at school? Let's imagine two students taking an exam. To pass the test they have to get 100 percent correct. Jason is very clever and always gets high grades. But Chris doesn't do very well and usually gets low grades.

They both take the test. Jason gets 99%, but Chris only gets 68%. Jason laughs at Chris and calls him stupid because of his low grades. Remember, the passing mark was 100% – **they both failed.** Coming close isn't good enough because a miss is as good as a mile. In other words – if you missed only by an inch, it might as well have been a mile — you still missed. That is why **we cannot get to heaven on our own – no matter how hard we try.**

Let me tell you

another story that will help you to understand.

There were two men that had to try and jump across a chasm with a river full or crocodiles at the bottom. The chasm was 30 feet wide. One man was very strong and physically fit — like Arnold Schwarzenegger. The other man was not fit at all and was really over weight. In fact he weighed about 450 pounds. They went away and practiced for a few weeks until the day finally came for them to try and jump across. A large crowd had gathered to watch the event. The strong man looked fitter and stronger than ever — even his muscles had muscles. The fat man had lost a little weight, about 8 pounds. He was, however, still too heavy and out of condition. The fat man began to run. He got to the edge of the chasm and jumped as hard as he could, but he only jumped about 7 feet and landed in the river where the crocodiles soon ate him up. Then the champion began to run. Faster and faster he went. The crowd watched in breathless anticipation. He gave a giant leap and soared up into the sky in a kind of arc. As he moved through the air the crowd began to roar with excitement. He had just passed 27 feet and broke the world record. No one had ever jumped that far before.

On and on he flew through the air and finally jumped 29 feet 9 inches! But it was 30 feet across — down he went into the water and the crocodiles came and gobbled him up.

The point of these stories is to show you that no matter how hard we try, we cannot get across the chasm into heaven on our own.

> **The only way to do it is for God to put a bridge across — so we can go across the bridge.**

A CROSS? A BRIDGE? YES! ACROSS A BRIDGE!

Jesus died on *a cross*
which is *the bridge* to God and to heaven.
That is the way we must go:
"By way of the cross."
Not doing it ourselves, but by
letting Christ take over

QUESTIONS FOR YOU TO ANSWER!

1. How does the Bible say we are saved? (Ephesians 2:8-9)   *Circle the correct answer.*

   A.   By working
   B.   By baptism
   C.   By grace
   D.   By communion
   E.   By Bible study

2. What score do we have to achieve to get to heaven??   *Circle the correct answer.*

   A.   68%
   B.   99%
   C.   100%

3. Why isn't getting close good enough?   *Fill in the blank line.*

_____

4. What is the bridge that crosses the ditch?   *Circle the correct answer.*

   A.   A rope bridge
   B.   A giant suspension bridge
   C.   The cross
   D.   A man-made floating bridge

A little while back we quoted a scripture in Ephesians that said we were saved by grace.

What is **GRACE?** . . . Well, for one thing –
God's **grace** is the *opposite* of works (trying to do it yourself).

GRACE is
God's mercy,
God's unmerited favor,
God's love.

It is *one* of God's Gifts to us!

> **"And if by grace, then it is no longer works; otherwise grace is no longer grace. But if it is works, it is no longer grace; otherwise work is no longer work."**
> *Romans 11:6*

What the Bible is saying is that we cannot get to heaven by both works and grace. If we are saved by God's grace, then what we do by good or bad behavior makes no difference — otherwise it can't be grace. On the other hand, if we were saved by works alone, then there would not be any grace. Jesus would not have died for us and we would have to make ourselves worthy for heaven by what we do. As you know, we have already seen that we can't do that. The apostle Paul went on to say that God's grace was bigger and more power-ful than our weakness or sin. There were some people, who when they

heard that, said, "Great! We can just keep on sinning because the more we sin the bigger God's grace will be." Paul replied to them with, "You don't know what you are saying, God forbid! How can you who have been saved by God's wonderful grace continue to sin willfully or think about doing such a thing?"

(Romans 6:1-2)

WORK

Although we are saved by grace alone, that does not mean we are free to do whatever we feel — or just be the same as everybody else. When we become a Christian, **we are saved**. As we continue as Christians, **we are being saved**. And when we finally go to heaven, **we have been saved**.

Some kids pray a sinners prayer for salvation and then go on behaving in the same old way as they had been before they prayed. That's being a phoney — and God will not accept that. Parents sometimes try to force their kids to behave like Christians, but as soon as they are not around the kids go back to behaving badly — just like non-believing kids.

Children! We cannot change you into true Christians by telling you to say prayers and by taking you to church and making you behave properly. **This must come from your own heart and desire.** Children must know and love God for themselves and not just to please their parents – and guess what! **YOU CAN** *KNOW GOD* **AND** *EXPERIENCE HIS POWER* **WHEN YOU BELIEVE.**

QUESTIONS FOR YOU TO ANSWER!

1. What is Grace? *Circle the correct answer.*

   A. What you pray before meals.
   B. A girl's name.
   C. God's kindness and mercy.
   D. Being good.

2. What is the opposite of Grace? *Circle the correct answer.*

   A. Works
   B. The Devil
   C. Children's church
   D. Being good

3. How can we get to heaven? *Circle the correct answer.*

   A. By works and Grace
   B. By works alone
   C. By hoping
   D. By Grace alone

4. What happens after being saved by Grace? *Circle the correct answer.*

   A. We carry on the same.
   B. We enjoy the day like a birthday.
   C. We continue being saved and look forward to finally being saved.
   D. We get saved once and then forget about it.
   E. We get lost everytime we sin and saved again when we repent.

Too many kids think it is easier to be like everybody else than to be different. Jesus said that there were two roads in life that we can take – one is a broad (wide) road that leads to destruction and the other is a narrow road that leads to eternal life (Matthew 7-13-14).

The broad way to destruction is like an interstate highway. There are many, many people, including kids, traveling on that route. **Why would they do that —**

Why???????

First of all, *it is downhill.*

Everybody knows that it is easier to peddle a bicycle down hill. In fact, if the road is real steep you don't have to peddle much at all. And the longer you are going downhill the faster you go and the more difficult it is to put on the brakes. The downhill way is harder for adults to get saved — especially if they are old. They have been on that road so long they don't know how to put the brakes on. At the end of the road there is a giantsize pit to fall into called **the Lake of Fire – HELL**. You don't have to be real bad to stay on that wide road, just be like most other people.

HELL —
The Lake of Fire

The narrow way is uphill.

The narrow way is uphill – and it is hard to peddle up hill! It makes your legs ache and that may tempt you to give up. But God has made an extra provision for those who travel uphill – for those who are not going down into the pit – but up into heaven. He provides an engine that attaches to the back of your bicycle. Although you have to keep on peddling, it becomes easier because the power of the engine really does the work. That's what we call the Holy Spirit. When you get off the broad way and onto the narrow way, you are accepting Christ and become a Christian. And when you fit that engine on the back of your bicycle you are asking and receiving the Holy Spirit's power.

Some kids say, "I'm not on the broad road and I'm not on the narrow road – I'm just sitting on the fence watching everybody go by or, "I have made a little path just for me to travel on.

The trouble with that idea is that there is no fence. **If we are not on God's narrow way, then we are on that broad road that leads to destruction.**

There are only two roads. Everybody is on one road — or the other!

Evangelists like me, are God's servants who call out to kids who are travelling on the wrong road and say,

"Quick! Quick! Get off the bad road and get on the right road — while there is still time."

QUESTIONS FOR YOU TO ANSWER!

1. How many roads are there?   *Fill in the blank line.*

_____

2. What road must a person take to be a Christian?   *Fill in the blank line.*

_____

3. What should people do who are on the broad road?   *Circle the correct answer.*

   A. Drive faster
   B. Put the brakes on
   C. Crash into other vehicles
   D. Get on the right road (the narrow road) while there is still time
   E. Park at a rest area

4. What does God give us to help us on the narrow road?   *Circle the correct answer.*

   A. A push
   B. A ten-speed bike
   C. A strong wind
   D. An engine/power

5. What is this engine that God gives us?   *Circle the correct answer.*

   A. A good talking to
   B. Some encouragement
   C. The Holy Spirit
   D. A helping hand

Remember children - the Christian life is a journey — like the famous story of the person named Christian in the book *Pilgrims Progress* by John Bunyan. If you have never read it, maybe you could ask your parents to get you a copy. They may even have a children's edition in your local Christian bookstore.

As Christians we must be careful that we do not settle down too much in this world and get caught up with all the fun things such as hobbies and sports that interest us and forget to put Jesus first in our lives. You see, our life is His life now. Because we are going on a journey we will face many temptations and obstacles — some of them will be the Devil's attacks and others will be allowed by God in order that we may learn to overcome them and be strong.

Let us be like the men and women of faith, in the Old Testament, who saw themselves as strangers and pilgrims who were looking for a better country and a better home built by God (Hebrews 11:13-16). Satan has succeeded in getting many kids to turn traitor and join his camp as they get older. Those kids may not think they are serving Satan, but many are. You don't have to join a satanist church to follow the Devil. All you have to do is to goof off and jump into the ways of the world and stop being faithful to Jesus.

The Lord has promised He will protect you and keep you, but you must stay close to Him and grow in your love for Him. Remember that it cost Him everything to save you. **You are very precious to Him.** The Bible says that God is very jealous over His children (Exodus 20:5, II Corinthians 11:2).

He certainly does not want to share you with the Devil.

I believe a good meaning for the word CHRISTIAN is **Anointed Warrior**.

Young Anointed Warrior stay faithful to your Lord and you will share in His glory!

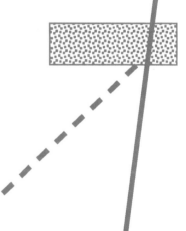

QUESTIONS FOR YOU TO ANSWER!

1. What is the Christian life like?   *Circle the correct answer.*

   A. A game
   B. A job
   C. A journey

2. What will we face on this journey?   *Circle the correct answer.*

   A. No problems
   B. Temptations and obstacles
   C. Lots of fun
   D. Rest stops

3. Where will the temptations and obstacles come from?   *Circle the correct answer.*

   A. Our enemies
   B. The Devil
   C. Our friends
   D. God
   E. Our parents

4. Who will allow us to be tempted?   *Circle the correct answer.*

   A. The Devil
   B. Ourselves
   C. Others
   D. God

5. Why does God allow us to be tempted?   *Circle the correct answer.*

   A. To wipe us out
   B. So we can fail
   C. So we may overcome, grow and be strong
   D. So we may give up

6. What is a good meaning for the word CHRISTIAN?

   A. A religious nut
   B. An anointed warrior
   C. A church goer
   D. A believer in God

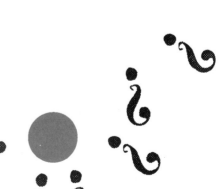

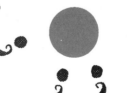

IMPORTANT!
NO CHEATING!
CHEATING IS A SIN. You are not to look at these answers until you have completed the questions.

CHAPTER ONE — Page 4

1. A new creature
2. To help your friends become Christians
3. To become a new creature
4. The new creature

CHAPTER TWO — Page 8

1. Good news
2. Not at all
3. By being born of God
4. To expose our weakness and sinfulness

CHAPTER THREE — Page 11

1. By receiving God's supernatural power
2. By really believing
3. That which trusts God with all of our hearts
4. The Lord Jesus

CHAPTER FOUR — Page 16 - 17

1. Jesus was
2. Because He was sinless
3. So that He can live for us
4. By living in us
5. See ourselves as crucified and dead
6. You rise up in Christ's perfect life
7. Making Jesus first and self last

CHAPTER FIVE — Page 22

1. By grace
2. 100%
3. A miss is as good as a mile
4. The Cross

CHAPTER SIX — Page 26

1. God's kindness and mercy
2. Works
3. Grace alone
4. We continue being saved and look forward to finally being saved

CHAPTER SEVEN — Page 31

1. Two
2. The narrow road
3. Get on the right road (the narrow road while there is still time)
4. An engine/power
5. The Holy Spirit

CHAPTER EIGHT — Page 35

1. A journey
2. Temptation and obstacles
3. The Devil
4. God
5. So we may overcome, grow and be strong
6. An anointed warrior

RAISING A GENERATION OF
ANOINTED CHILDREN AND YOUTH

ONE-DAY TRAINING SEMINAR

Equipping Parents, Youth Pastors, Sunday School Teachers and Children's Workers

The churches in your area can experience one of these dynamic seminars. Author and speaker David Walters imparts a fresh vision and anointing to parents and to those who work with children and youth. Walters says:

Children do not have a baby or junior Holy Spirit!

Children are baptized in the Holy Spirit to do much more than play, be entertained or listen to a few moral object lessons!

The average church-wise child can be turned around and <u>set on fire for God!</u>

Christian teenagers do not have to surrender to peer pressure — they can become the peers!.